The Pioneer PT Prototype

The Ultimate Guide to Building Your Mobile Health & Wellness Studio

The Pioneer PT Prototype

The Ultimate Guide to Building Your Mobile Health & Wellness Studio

James Dulkerian, DPT

Dedication

To my Dad, Jim Dulkerian. You are the man!

Your support has been undeniable. I am so grateful, not only that you have always been there, but for your willingness to help bring my dreams to reality. I am forever grateful to you for going on this wild journey with me, and will never forget the bond we have built during this process.

You have taught me a lot, and I hope that I too can possess the ability to be there for my family as you have always been there for me.

Table of Contents

Acknowledgements:

I am so grateful for my entire family, and their support on this journey. Sherry Dulkerian thank you for being my cheerleader when times were tough. Thank you Blaine Dulkerian, for showing me what strength really is, and Pop, Charles Fick, for your amazing expertise in woodworking. Thank you to the rest of my family and neighbors who contributed as well.

To my future wife, Anita Klimanis, thank you for believing in me and putting up with my non-stop talk and work to make this dream a reality. I look forward to a future together.

Thank you Josh Payne for challenging me and pushing me to get my dream out to the world. I am excited to see more health and wellness professionals say HELL NO to the system and instead bring convenient, personalized, and preventive HEALTH-care to people around the world, by saying no to sickcare!

Forward by Josh Payne

When I work with healthcare providers to help them to grow their practices, I always ask one question when helping to guide them: If you were given five million dollars tomorrow, and money was not an issue for you, what type of patient would you still want to see?

I ask this question because it quickly helps someone to pinpoint their passion. And Passion is what drives a person to do incredible things in their life. You see, fulfillment and passion, is what is missing for most burned out healthcare professionals. We go into grad school with so much wonder and possibility! Then, a few years after we get punched in the face by the real world, we sometimes find ourselves burnt out and trying to figure out a new way.

That is why that first question is so important in the current healthcare climate. We need more fulfillment and passion to fill our days, and guide what we do. J.T.'s answer to that question was immediately "Mountain Bikers". I remember sitting there on the other end of the zoom call just thinking and strategizing with him. There are amazing possibilities for a mobile van that serves mountain bikers in the community. The possibilities are endless!

As I write this, it is almost exactly one year ago that J.T. and I started working together to grow his mobile practice. It has been an absolute pleasure to grow a friendship with him, and see him to have success in his life.

I'll never forget the first conversation that I had with J.T. over the phone about his practice. I was astonished, and had never heard of anyone starting a physical therapy practice that was truly mobile! Not only that, but a pretty sweet van and setup. What astonished me the most was how driven he was to prove this model successful.

We need more healthcare professionals to have the same passion for what they do as J.T. does. That's why this book needed to be written, and needs to be read by you. If you want to fuel your career with passion and fulfillment, you need to read this book. J.T. has done the heavy lifting for you, all you have to do is use this book as your guide. Read this book, put it into action, and see the impact your mobile studio will have on your community. I can't wait to see it.

J.T., thank you for providing us with this incredible resource to allow other healthcare professionals to become "unstuck" and start their own truly mobile health and wellness studio.

Josh Payne
Author of The Concierge PT
Success Formula

The Pioneer PT Prototype

Intro:

I know some of you are wondering how did you come up with the idea to start Pioneer PT, and how did you create the first mobile physical therapy and wellness studio? Some of you have even reported similar ideas. I know this because physical therapists, massage therapists, and other wellness practitioners have reached out individually from my hometown of Baltimore, Maryland, to across the country on the West coast, and even across the world to places I have only dreamed of going. In this book, I will teach you a step by step guide on how to build and create the mobile business of your dreams that will allow you the flexibility to see your ideal client where they are.

But, first I want to tell you WHY I decided to build a mobile wellness studio. I designed a mobile wellness studio, because I feel that healthcare should be Convenient so you are never stuck in a waiting room again, or forgotten about in the back room. I was once forgotten about in a back room for over an hour at the eye doctors, and this was after I had already waited 45 minutes in the waiting room. I began to wander around the hallways debating whether to leave, before someone finally came. This is unacceptable, and I feel should never happen to anyone! Time is precious and should be respected. I believe that care should also be Personalized, so that you are treated like an individual with a unique life experience with unique issues, and not cookie cutter care by a professional who is "burnt out," and going through the motions. Most of all I believe that care should be Preventive, so that people continue to live an active lifestyle, and are not put on unnecessary pain medication or at risk of potentially harmful side effects from unnecessary surgery.

I can vividly remember a past client of mine when I was the clinic director at a local outpatient sports medicine clinic. We will call him "Mr. Smith" for the sake of this story. Mr. Smith was referred by an orthopedic surgeon due to back pain and leg symptoms. I saw him on and off for a few years. We would eliminate his leg symptoms and back pain except for the most energetic tasks such as yard work, which created temporary mild soreness only in his lower back. Despite education, Mr. Smith would stop doing his home exercise program when he was feeling good between each course of physical therapy, and would eventually come back the following year with an exacerbation of his pain.

However, the last time Mr. Smith came back to physical therapy, it was completely different. As recommended by his surgeon, Mr. Smith decided to undergo a lumbar fusion surgery with the expectation that surgery would eliminate his pain forever. However, the results were quite the opposite. Pain was still present, but with the addition of a very unfortunate side effect. He had damage during surgery that left him with right drop foot. He lost all strength in his ankle and had to utilize a device called an AFO to hold his foot up while walking to avoid tripping. This was tragic! It really disappointed me that he would now have to live the rest of his life with a true disability. It was difficult to portray an uplifting energy that Mr. Smith required to get through this unfortunate outcome. I constantly was thinking, "If only he would have continued with conservative physical therapy to manage his symptoms this never would have happened!." I felt terrible for him. Many of you may have experienced something very similar to what had happened to Mr. Smith, and understand the power of conservative care or preventative treatment.

Benjamin Franklin once said, "An ounce of prevention is worth a pound of cure." To me this means it is easier to stop something from happening in the first place, than to repair the damage after something has already happened.

Fortunately, Mr. Smith's story is something that I envision can and will one day be a thing of the past. But, it requires your help and proper education to our clients! We must be the first point of service to keep people well for a lifetime.

Something else you may be wondering, "Does a mobile physical therapy studio really work? Can this be a viable business model? What is your background and why did you choose to go mobile instead of a traditional brick and mortar clinic? How does this really relate to health and wellness? Maybe he is just another crazy van lifer."

My answer is without a doubt, YES! A mobile physical therapy studio works! Not only does it work, but it gives you the freedom to deliver personalized, convenient, and preventative care on your terms. You will have the opportunity to see less clients, spend more time doing the things that YOU love, and make more money. Providing care that society currently only expects for pro athletes or the elite will become the norm. Those who value their health can easily justify an out-of-network expense to live their best life. As Randy Moss once said, "Straight cash homie!"

Also, despite my love for travel and my mobile studio "Big Blue," no, I do not live in my van. Hahaha!

Everyone knows that we are now living in the age of convenience. Everyone wants products and services delivered directly to them when they want. We live in the Amazon age of convenience. How many people that you know have Amazon Prime?

You have seen food trucks for years, but more recently you may have noticed an increase in mobile services offered for pets, including mobile veterinarians, and mobile dog groomers. Well, what about people? You can get your food, your haircut, and custom tailored clothing delivered to you. You can have your car washed, detailed, and the oil changed while you are at work or asleep. But, what about health and wellness that is tailored for you, shouldn't that be delivered too? Fortunately, Pioneer PT has you covered.

Why not mobile physical therapy, massage therapy, personal training, acupuncture, occupational therapy, reiki, etc.? The options are endless, and THIS will be the next frontier in the delivery of health and wellness services. It is a no brainer.

Why can't we receive care when and where we need it?
- Forget calling the doctor and being put on a waiting list for a couple weeks, or even months before being seen.
- Forget waiting in a waiting room for over an hour or forgot about in the back room.
- Forget the rushed 15 minute appointment in which you didn't even have the chance to get all your questions and concerns addressed.
- Forget feeling like nothing but a number &
- Forget not being able to stay active for a lifetime.

Clients don't have to feel like all the doctor is seeing is dollar signs when they look at them anymore! That is bullshit care from an antiquated system! The traditional physical therapy clinic is stuck in the past! It is something that I am truly embarrassed to have been a part of at the end of my working career in a traditional setting, and I am so happy to have left that antiquated system behind. Let's do something about this together!

Here is your chance to really reach and connect with your ideal client where they need it most. You can provide compassionate and personalized care to your clients so that they no longer feel like a number, or just that "guy with a bad right knee." You will have the chance to build meaningful relationships with your clients that can last a lifetime.

Sure, there are typical places to see clients. The most typical place to see someone is at their home or office, but I challenge you to get creative! Maybe your target market would benefit from service at a local running event, swim meet, fall festival, tournament, state park, golf course, trail, park and ride, or the shopping mall. The options are endless, but can and should be tailored towards the people that you can best serve, as well as those who you enjoy working with the most. I would argue that these go hand in hand. That way it never feels like a day of work again!

You might be thinking, are these mobile services already offered? Probably not. There is really no competition! There has been an increase in mobile service offerings, but not as prevalent as you would think, and not with the convenience of a mobile studio. The mobile studio negates any set up time, or lugging a heavy massage table around. It allows you to bring everything you need with you, and helps create a peaceful and private setting for your client.

Your client won't feel embarrassed in an open clinic full of clients and staff, with their rear end hanging out when you are working on their lower back. Don't make your client feel "In Bare Assed."

Personally, I have helped many working mothers who remarked about the convenience of being able to receive care on their lunch break while at work so that they can get home to their children, or make it to their children's events after work. This helps parents avoid child care disasters or feeling like they are missing out on their children's lives. These are just a couple examples of why clients enjoy the mobile studio, but don't forget your true target market. Where can you serve your ideal client the best? This will help you stand out from the competition. Working mothers are not necessarily my target market, but just because you typically serve one particular group, does not mean you won't end up treating and helping others as well. Word of mouth is very powerful.

Pioneer PT's target market is outdoor enthusiasts, and I bring care to cycling, and running events in the Baltimore, Maryland metro area. Pioneer PT has even been spotted at the trailhead. This is preventive care at the source of where people need it most, letting people know that you are there for them. When Pioneer PT expands out west, the plan is to service the beach for surfers, and the trailhead for mountain bikers and endurance athletes.

As a sub niche we see business owners and executives that crave personalized care at their home. This helps create accountability for their strength and wellness so that these business owners can perform their high stress jobs to the best of their abilities. You must be healthy in order to sustain a high profile job for the long term. Again, get creative with your target market and be there where they need care most. It is a beautiful thing!

To Do List:

- Write down who you enjoy working with most & who you can best help
- Why you like working with this group most
- What does this ideal client or "avatar" look like
- Where does my ideal client hang out

How Did This Idea Start?

In short, this idea started because I was being fed up with the status quo of an outdated physical therapy system that was stuck in the 80's, an epic road trip, and a dream that got the wheels spinning, or maybe it was just all that Rage Against The Machine that I listened to growing up?

It was a crazy dream and has been an even crazier ride. I could never have imagined that I would be where I am today. I have been a doctor of physical therapy for over 10 years and have always dreamed about the opportunity to run my own business. I never imagined it would be in this capacity, with a mobile studio, serving people at their convenience.

I also never knew I would have the chance to positively impact so many people around the country and around the world. I am now a proud business owner of the first mobile physical therapy studio called, Pioneer PT. I get to serve the exact population that I relate with most, and am excited to work with every day. They are outdoor enthusiasts. I am happy with my career for the first time in years. I have more freedom with my schedule, I am about to get married, start a family, and live a life I have always envisioned. Family is something that is super important for me, and I want to be there for my kids someday as my parents were there for me. Now, all of this will be possible, because I am the boss!

My Goal:

I can only provide care to a limited number of clients myself, and my goal has evolved to a much greater scale. My goal is to help thousands of health and wellness practitioners around the world provide high quality personalized, preventive, and convenient care to their clients via a mobile studio so that they too can live a life by design. I know it sounds cliche, but like I did, I want you to fall in love with your career once more so that you never have to work a day in your life again. Let's change the face of healthcare forever!

The Story Behind Pioneer PT:

After contemplating the question a bit longer, how did Pioneer PT begin? I believe that everything in my life has brought me to this point of launching the first mobile physical therapy studio with a doctor of physical therapy that travels directly to the client to provide the best possible service. It is truly direct care.

Years before I knew I wanted to be a physical therapist, I had a sense of small business instilled in me as a child. Both my mother's and father's parents owned small businesses. My grandmother on my mom's side of the family owned both a flower shop in Ocean City, and a clothing store in Towson, while my grandfather owned a successful door manufacturing business in Baltimore.

However, it was my father's family business, Dulkerian's Persian Rug Co. that made the largest impact on my life. I helped my dad regularly while growing up when school was out. We were the classic Armenian family who owned a Persian rug shop that sold, stored, washed, and mended handmade rugs. My grandmother repaired rugs for years before retiring, and eventually my dad took over for my grandfather. My Dad still runs the shop, and it is now in the third generation. It was originally started by my great grandfather in 1921 who escaped Armenia during the genocide in the early 1900's.

Getting up and commuting an hour into Baltimore every day to wash dirty rugs for a living will definitely make you humble. However, it was something I was very proud of. My dad worked so hard to support his family and to help people out. He has always made it more convenient for customers with pick ups, deliveries, and sales directly to his customers out of his blue work van. I watched my father work so hard physically, and knew I wanted something more. He too wanted more for me, and encouraged me to go to college .

Growing up in a middle class family, I was always taught to get a good education, and a college degree as this would allow me to get a good job. My father dropped out of college to pursue the family business, and my mom got an associates degree. My parents wanted my little sister, Blaine, and I to achieve a higher level of education so that we could get better jobs and would not have to struggle like they did. This is the middle class mindset. Only this past year did I realize that this mindset was just a self limiting belief of the middle class. The possibilities are truly endless with the proper mindset.

I found physical therapy in my junior year of high school, and I knew without a doubt that it was what I wanted to do for a living. I also knew that this career would allow me a chance to someday own my own business. The autonomy is why I chose physical therapy over physician assistant, nursing, or pharmacy. I never believed in pushing pills, so pharmacy was out. I also knew that cleaning bodily fluids and needles weren't for me. A physician assistant would have been cool, but may not have offered the autonomy I was seeking.

I worked hard and ended up going to Ithaca College to study physical therapy. This was when I met the most influential person in my young career: my professor Ernie Nalette. He always talked about the profession of physical therapy and how it really was in the real world. He became my mentor, influencing me to question the status quo, and to always provide what was best for my patients. Physical therapy should not be an assembly line, packing as many people as possible into a day. I took his advice to heart, but worked on honing my knowledge and skills over the past decade, becoming very proficient in hands-on techniques in rehabilitation.

I worked my way up the corporate ladder as a director of an outpatient sports medicine clinic for 7 years. Despite greater experience, better outcomes, and a managerial role in the company, I began to realize that I had hit my ceiling. I hit the ceiling for growth in the company, with salary, as well as the ability to make decisions that really matter, like what is best for my clients health.

Then there was one particular day that I will never forget. I was working with a client, right smack in the middle of a busy day, when my boss walked in. I was thinking, "Uh oh, what does he want?" I knew immediately there was a problem, because no one ever saw him when things were going well. What could it be? I pride myself on giving great care, achieving results, and I know I build lasting relationships with my clients.

I had to excuse myself and sat down with my boss. He proceeded to tell me that I had to change the way that I was treating clients. He told me that I would need to see more people in a day, spend less time with my clients, get them to exercise in groups, and bill more charges. If I did not, I would never get a raise. In my head I was thinking "How am I ever to build and be there for a family of my own, like my parents were there for me, if I was at work for 12 hours a day?" This thought just infuriated me more! WTF!?!? I began to fire back, " I do what is right for my clients and achieve great results! That is no longer important to you? I will not compromise care for the bottom line! I wondered if I would get fired, but didn't even care, because I was checked out at this point. Little did I know, this was the conversation that would change my life forever.

I realized that I was merely middle management getting shit on by both ends first by the boss, and then those who I managed. This was because, the company I worked for was bought out and the whole reason WHY the company existed in the first place was lost. The new ownership was only concerned about the bottom line. How could I lead people when the identity of the company was gone?

What I experienced is the middle class lie! I was experiencing the pains of coming out of college with 6 figures of student loan debt, which is like a mortgage payment every month, but having the expectation that a stable career would be able to support me. The tough realization was that this situation would not actually be substantial enough for me to get ahead in life. Someone would always be in control of my schedule, my pay, and in turn my life.

Throughout my career I have continually heard about the decreases in reimbursement from insurance companies from my superiors. I have experienced the cutting of my benefits, and the inability to receive a raise for years at a time, despite my hard work and excellent patient outcomes. I always heard the same story that we must see more patients in order to survive. At the same time patients have seen increased deductibles and copays. The decreasing reimbursements from insurance companies were always the owners excuse when it came to forcing you to see more people in a workday, or attempt to influence you to treat and bill a certain way that pays more. Excuse my language, but again that is bullshit! Why is healthcare lead with a fear based mentality? That is not right!

Bottom line, I am doing what is best for the client, not just what reimburses more. I feel that insurance based business is unethical due to these outside pressures. I wanted something better for my clients. They are people, and should not be put through an assembly line of crappy care with warm up on the exercise bike, work with them for 15 minutes, then pass them off to a tech who is a high school kid that trained on the job, and finish the visit with electrical stimulation, just to see a new person every 15-30 minutes all day long. What kind of life is that? Surely not one that I was willing to settle for personally or professionally for my clients. My ethics and reputation are important to me.

After wallowing in my sorrow I thought I needed to do something to cheer up. This was when I took a once in a lifetime trip along the California coastline camping, surfing, and hiking along the way via a 1984 Volkswagen Vanagon named Lone Star from Vintage Surfari Wagons.

Thank goodness my fiancé and I were there before the 2017 mudslide, because that was the same exact stretch of road in the Big Sur that we boondocked for the night to watch the sunset over the cliffs on the Pacific coast highway. Boondocking is illegal, but it was gorgeous and a memory that will last a lifetime. I would highly recommend this drive at least once in your life. You will not regret it!

Anyway, I am sorry to get side tracked, but I started seeing a ton of DIY camper vans on the trip. I loved the concept and originally thought that I wanted to build out a surf, mountain bike, camper van for myself for weekend getaways. This would at least help me through the tough weeks of work with something fun to look forward to on the weekends. But, who wants to live for the weekends? I wanted to feel fulfilled, and LIVE every single day.

What happened next just seemed magical. I experienced a moment in life that was my calling, like a light bulb went off. I woke up wide awake in the middle of the night, at about 2 in the morning, just having experienced a vivid dream about the concept of a mobile physical therapy studio. There are food trucks, there are mobile vets, why not a mobile rehabilitation studio for people. It was my "ah ha" moment!

I quickly realized that it may be possible to create a mobile studio that I could take directly to clients, with everything that I needed inside to provide the best quality care at the client's convenience. Care would also be personalized, and preventive being the first on the scene as the physical therapy profession desired. I made it my mission, putting in a ton of hard work and planning, even traveling all the way to the Lone Star State of Texas to purchase my big blue van. From scratch, I built out my van into a physical therapy studio on wheels thanks to the help from my family. Pioneer PT was born!

My original goal was to help as many folks in the Baltimore metro area that I could, by providing the best possible care directly to my clients. Now, my goals have changed and gotten much much larger.

My mission is to share this dream, and help thousands of other health and wellness professionals around the world to light a fire inside, and provide a level of service that will change healthcare forever.

I want your help!

How A Mobile Studio Can Benefit You:

You will be surprised with the amount of freedom that a mobile studio will bring to your life. You will without a doubt stand out in your community, because no one else is doing this. The opportunities are endless with the events that you can cover from races, to golf courses, to the local trail head, and to corporate offices just to name a few. Let your imagination and opportunity take you where you can best serve your ideal client. Some of the benefits will be highlighted below.

No/low rent:

One of the other largest benefits of a mobile studio is low overhead compared to a brick and mortar location. You do not have to worry about rent after the vehicle is paid off. Depending on your car loan, after ~5-7 years at the very most, you will no longer have payments and only have to pay for fuel and maintenance. If you do well, and put money back into the business by paying the mobile studio off sooner, then this will just prolong the possibility for profit. To give you an idea, I did put some money down (~10K), but my payments are $645 per month. This is much cheaper than renting a brick and mortar location. For example if you charge $150 per visit, this works out to just under one client visit per week for the year. Does that sound doable?

Otherwise, when starting out, you would be looking at trying to lock in a deal by only paying per client or per hour of use for a shared workspace. But, you are stuck in one place and have to deal with growing pains with increasing rent with increased time in the space, and then potentially moving locations as you grow. Build out costs are necessary in both a brick and mortar location and the van, so either way you will have to include that into your start up costs.

Large Radius:

Another huge benefit of a mobile studio is that you do not have to market solely within a 5 mile radius around your brick and mortar location, you can market to the entire town or even city. This all depends on how far you are willing to drive. This allows you to service different areas, different gyms, different golf courses, different apartment complexes. The options are endless. You have the option of charging for travel if it is out of your distance, or just having them meet you somewhere within your service area. I prefer to build the cost of travel into my price per visit. Think outside the box and you will succeed.

Flexibility!

Flexibility is key, not only for your clients, but for you. You now have control of your schedule. You can schedule in that lunch break that you never had when working for someone else, you can be home for your family and children when you want. You have the freedom to live the lifestyle you wish, whether it is hitting dawn patrol every morning, or the trails after work. Shoot! You could even see your clients at the golf course if you wish. Being able to be and treat outside the confines of four walls is amazing. You are never locked inside a building all day long, without windows. You are free to take your treatment sessions outside and breathe the fresh air. It does wonders for you and your clients wellbeing. You could even bring your dog to work, which is also proven to improve mental health.

<u>Options:</u>

There are more options with a mobile studio than just a mobile concierge service using your car. You are not limited to a specific location where you can see clients. It is not necessary for a client to have a private office at work, their own private gym, or even access to a gym at all. I always give my clients the option of being seen in their home, or in the mobile studio, and the majority of the time they rather be seen in the mobile studio. Everyone has their reasons, but I have heard everything from their house is dirty, their dogs will cause trouble, to it is peaceful place that they can focus on themselves for one hour out of the day without distractions.

How beneficial would it be for you to be in control of your schedule? To have options? Do you desire a certain lifestyle? I know I do, and that was a consideration when building the business of my dreams.

Things To Consider:

There are many things to consider when starting any business, but I want to go over some of the main things to consider when starting a service-based business with a mobile studio.

You must consider the area you propose to start this business. How is the weather? Does it snow regularly, are there a lot of hills, is there parking available, how hot and cold does it get, and who do you plan to see with the mobile studio?

Weather:

If there are only a handful of days that it snows significantly like Maryland, where I live, then you can get away with rear wheel drive. The worst days with over a few inches on the road, I call a snow day, and reschedule my clients to another day. The snow usually does not last long on the road around here. I do this because I am thinking long term. Yes, there is something to be said when you can get to your clients in any weather, no matter what. That is customer service! However, I want you to ask yourself, is it worth it? When you are starting out you only have one vehicle on the road, and it is not worth getting in an accident. That truck is your livelihood. If your mobile studio is in the shop, then that will throw a serious wrench in your schedule, potentially losing visits.

However, if you live in the northeast or the mountains out west such as Colorado then you must definitely consider 4 wheel drive. If you plan to regularly attend events like a cyclocross or steeplechase race and park in a muddy field, then again you should at least consider a 4 wheel drive vehicle. 4 Wheel drive does come at a significantly greater cost at about 5-8K extra, depending on vehicle brand, but you will get a badass adventure vehicle. One other thing to consider with a 4 wheel drive vehicle is that the entry height is slightly higher than the rear wheel drive version of a Sprinter, creating an even higher step to get into and out of the mobile studio. The increase in height of the entrance is definitely another factor to consider.

The terrain:

Do you want to start this business where the terrain is relatively flat? If so you are golden! However, if you live in San Francisco or an area that has limited parking then you may want to consider your options. These vehicles can drive on hilly roads without a problem, but when parked and working with a client you should be parked on a flat area. If the road has a lot of camber in the middle and you are parked on the side of the road, the treatment area will be tilted towards the side. If you park on a hill then the treatment area will be sloped forward or backward depending on the hill. It is best to find a fairly flat parking area for treatment. Fortunately there are a couple options.

First, automatic vehicle leveling devices can be purchased and installed under the vehicle similar to RV's, and level the vehicle at the touch of a button. However, you can also get creative with this issue depending on the level of service that you want to deliver. For example, in a very busy downtown area with limited parking I have been known to pick clients up from the door of their office building, take the client to an area with plentiful parking and a view of the inner harbor here in Baltimore, work with them, and then have the client back to their workplace within an hour. Other ideas, I have met people at a park and ride, the mall parking lot, a local park, all for treatment at their convenience, when and where it was most suitable for them. Normally visits occur at the client's home, or office. Just get creative and you may be surprised at some of the places that you will see a client throughout your career.

Substantial parking must be available:

There are options, but this mobile studio is LOONNGG! My vehicle is ~15 feet inside the treatment area, not including the cockpit/seats, and engine. It does not fit length wise in a normal spot. Typically it is best to find parking at the back of the lot with sufficient area room behind the spot where the back of the vehicle can hang over into the grass, etc. Backing into a spot is easy with the use of the large mirrors and back up camera, which are fantastic. Otherwise you will be looking for two spots front to back and take up two due to the length of the vehicle. There are 144 and 170 inch wheelbase versions of the popular Mercedes Sprinter van. The 170 inch version is almost 23 feet long! The 170 inch is the version that I used for the build out. It allowed me to create an ample 15 feet of treatment area inside the vehicle. The 144 inch wheelbase does have its advantages too being easier to park, better gas milage, and only about a 4 foot difference in inside studio space.

Vehicle height also goes along with substantial parking. You must consider the height of the vehicle to avoid potential damage. In order to accommodate people over 6 feet tall to stand up inside and reach overhead, you must purchase a high roof. This allows you to provide ample height to work with most people standing up, and still being able to jump for functional testing and plyometrics, or reach overhead. Prior to 2017 Mercedes labeled this height of the vehicle the super high roof. Now, if you plan to work with just basketball players or tall football players that are all 6'6" or taller then you may want to consider another option if working on their upper extremities. These folks will not be able to reach overhead adequately.

I mention height strongly, because there are limitations here. You cannot park in a parking garage, because you will not fit. You cannot go under certain low hanging limbs on the side of the road. Overgrowth does happen certain times of the year. This does not apply to most highways or major roadways that trucks typically utilize, but you have to be careful especially on neighborhood roads, and make sure you drive towards the midline of the road in these situations so you don't give your mobile studio a damaging buzzcut. I prefer the mullet look, business in the front, party in the back! Haha!

I mention this information to you, because there is only one real blindspot in the Sprinter. That blindspot is above the view of your mirrors, and above the rear view camera. Unfortunately, I found this out the hard way, when backing into a spot. I did not consider the branches from the tree behind the spot. Plus they were out of view from the mirrors and the rear view camera. I guess sometimes you live and you learn, but it was a costly mistake. Not only did it require body work, but it also creates downtime when your truck is in the shop. Protect your mobile studio like it is your baby! I am happy to share my mistakes so these issues do not happen to you.

You will probably start with only one studio, so again protect it with your life. If you do not change the oil regularly, wash the vehicle, provide the required maintenance, or choose to drive recklessly then you are setting yourself up for failure. These are great vehicles, with a diesel engine that can run forever. Take care of it, and it will take care of you long after the vehicle is paid off. I have spoken to business owners with delivery fleets, and seen reports online of Sprinters going 300-500 thousand miles. As an example, just to be conservative, if you drive 20,000 miles per year, which is greater than the 15,000 mile average, you could drive for 10 years, and only reach 200,000 miles.

You will be looking at maintenance costs only for quite a few years after the vehicle is paid off. Hence, all profit!

Who do you plan to see in the mobile studio:

Again, consider the height of the individuals you plan to see. This will be one of the tallest vehicles that you can purchase on the road, but an NBA basketball team may not your best target market due to height restrictions. Do you plan to see a Medicare population? There are options to add a lift or ramp for this situation, but it would come at a cost. A detachable ramp would be much too large to store in the vehicle due to the required rise to run to safely walk into the mobile studio. The height is approximately 20 inches to get to the first step inside of the vehicle.

I have purchased an electric step option that comes out automatically when the sliding side door opens, which makes it two steps. It is an AMP Research power step running board. The first is an 8 inch step and the second is a 12 inch step. A 12 inch step is fairly large. I always hold my client's hand and require them to hold onto the grab bar when getting in and out of the vehicle for safety. I mention the step height every time someone steps in and out, just as a heads up to avoid the possibility of falls or injury. If your target market population cannot safely get in and out of the mobile studio there are other measures that can be taken. Instead I would suggest taking the necessary tools that you need into your client's home to provide a safe treatment. There are always solutions. This also leads into specific medical conditions or surgeries. If you see a lot of people early on in the rehabilitation process for something like a total knee replacement or ACL repair you may not want them stepping into the mobile studio until their are able to without the risk of injury. Instead start seeing these folks in their homes. They will value this convenience and your willingness to go above and beyond.

How cold or hot does the temperature get in your area?

This matters because you will have to consider heat and AC installation in the treatment area of the vehicle. In Maryland we require both because it gets extremely hot and humid during the summer with a high temperature around 100 degrees with air so thick it is like "soup", and then gets down close to 0 degrees in the winter with occasional heavy snow. These both come at an additional cost, and are the single costliest items when it comes to the build out process. However, they are necessary to keep the mobile studio both comfortable and professional.

Do it for the right reasons:

Alright, I want to vent a little bit here. Don't just do this because you think it will give you the salary you deserve, because people will see right through you. The number one reason you should consider a mobile studio is because you want to provide a patient centered experience for your clients. It is all about the service. You are doing this to provide the best possible treatment with preventive and personalized care, when and where your ideal client needs it. It is that simple. This is for the client. Truly a client centered practice. It cannot be just words like many other companies claim. Being genuine in who you are and your desire to help others first will then allow the benefits from mobile studio to flow your way and enrich your life.

Use your best Judgement:

Using your best judgement is another thing I want to touch on here. There is potential to work with pediatrics or adolescents, but please, please use your judgement and always have a parent stay with you for the duration of your session while working with your client. Also, women's health MAY be an issue here if there has been a past traumatic experience. No, this is not your 70's style van with shag carpet and a couch inside. Don't be that creepy guy that your parents always told you about as a kid, not to ever get in a stranger's vehicle or take candy from a stranger. If I find out there is anyone using the mobile studio concept with a predator mindset, if the law allows, I will personally find you and smack you down!!!

Maintenance:

This is something to strongly consider. Are you handy? Do you know how to change the oil, and are proficient with maintenance tasks for your vehicle. Will you do the maintenance yourself? Sometimes it can save a bit of time and money to do it yourself, but I want to point out a few key points that might have you thinking differently.

Yes, it can be costly to get serviced through the dealer, but if anything goes wrong due to their work, it is on them. They cannot blame anyone but themselves if something goes wrong. They have insurance for these errors that will cover you in an emergency. This is crucial, because I know, especially early on, I could not afford large repair bills for a Mercedes. A huge repair bill, literally could have put me out of business.

Also, you must consider, what is you time worth? What can you do with your time that you are not spending working on the vehicle? Could you be marketing? Maybe selling? Working on systems for your business or even online programing that can bring in money on its own? Everyone would love to have a secondary form of income. You could even see a client in their home with a portable massage table for the day and still get paid. Your time may very well be worth more than the money you save by doing the work yourself.

Also, this is a specialty vehicle. Many shops are not proficient in working on this type of vehicle, especially if it is something major, nor are they able to fit your vehicle in the shop. Most shops are unable to service this vehicle due to the sheer height of the vehicle.

Is it worth it to save a couple hundred dollars on routine service? Initially you might think yes, but looking back, I do not think so. My final recommendation, DO NOT do the maintenance work yourself. There are two options that may be best. You could pony up the extra coin for a service package at the time of purchase, or find a reputable shop that works on fleet vehicles for other businesses, and works with these vehicles regularly knowing them inside and out.

I found a business in my area where all the employees came from the dealership, are master mechanics, and many have 15 years of experience with Sprinter vans. These are the folks I trust with my mobile studio, and are cheaper than the dealer. These folks broke free from the dealership, as I broke free from the traditional physical therapy system, because we wanted better for our clients. It is also nice to support other local small businesses.

<u>Have you ever felt:</u>

- Burnt out?
- You have worked in the healthcare system for awhile, and have seen the ugly side of healthcare.
- You have been frustrated with the amount of time that you are allotted to spend with your patients and feel you treat them like a number with cookie-cutter treatments.
- You know that you can provide a higher level of service and care that gets people better faster
- If you are frustrated and feel like an embarrassment to your profession

At the end of my career in the traditional outpatient sports medicine clinic, I truly felt that way. I felt that massage therapists, chiropractors, and personal trainers were taking care of, and marketing to their clients so much better than we were able to in an insurance based setting in physical therapy. I applaud these other professions for their efforts. It was just a sad state of affairs in the physical therapy field. I did not get into the profession to give crappy care!

If you have felt these frustrations say, **"Hell yeah, I am ready to make a change!"**

How I Chose My Vehicle:

This was no easy task being the first to build out a mobile physical therapy studio. A lot of research went into this. I first called every van outfitter that I could find out there on the internet and got quotes on price anywhere from 150-300K for a custom build out. Ouch! That is ridiculous! I then began to drive around looking at a bunch of different vehicles noting the positives and negatives for each. I will review the positives and negatives of each below.

I looked at multiple different types of buses, box trucks, RV's, and trailers, and there was a problem with all of them. Transit buses were too big with terrible gas mileage and required a special license. Mini buses seemed cool on the outside, often with low handicap ramps to get in, but the ceiling height was limited. Many of these style buses sloped upward towards the back of the bus, creating an uneven floor. It would be necessary to build the floor up to a flat surface, which would only decrease head space even more. There definitely would not be any room for standing shoulder exercises or jumping as I could hardly stand up tall. Box trucks were an option, but they do not hold up as well long term and would require additional build out considerations. In order to have a large enough box on the frame for a proper sized treatment area, this would also require a larger truck with a special license. Then trailers… It was an option, but there is no possible electric unless a generator was built in, plus you have to own a truck that can pull a large trailer. I do not own a truck and that alone is a costly predicament. I really did not like the idea of putting people in a trailer either.

Then, I test drove both a Ford Transit and Mercedes Sprinter Van. Keep in mind this is a few years ago, models have changed, and vehicles were updated. At the time, the Ford was good, but the gas mileage was less, and the ceiling height was not as high. I am 6'3" and need some extra head room. Then came the Mercedes Sprinter Van, and as soon as I test drove it, I knew it was the one. It drove like a dream! It drove like a modern truck or an extended minivan, with large mirrors, safety features such as blind spot monitoring, cross wind assist, and an excellent back-up camera. It also had power in the V6 version, with some get up and go, to get on the highway safely. There were many different options due to their use as platforms for RVs, and most importantly the highest roof in it's class. This accommodates most people standing and exercising overhead. It was called the super high roof. I was sold, I just needed to find one for sale.

This was a story in itself, but I had already made the decision that I was going for this, and wanted to be the first to build out a proper mobile physical therapy studio. During this time it was shortly after the Volkswagen (VW) emissions scandal in 2015. If you do not remember, VW had programed their diesel TDI vehicles to activate their emissions controls only during laboratory emissions testing. Well they got busted, and the EPA decided to broaden their investigation and check other European diesel manufacturers as well including Mercedes Benz. Sooner or later you always get busted when you do the wrong thing. This shut down production and importation of diesel vehicles to the US, including the Mercedes Sprinter Van. I called every Mercedes dealer in the area, and they could not find a Sprinter van with the super high roof that I needed in the entire country.

I persisted and was able to find two at the same dealership in Austin, Texas. I had my eye on one in particular that was a V6 Mercedes Sprinter with a super high roof among other desirable options for a build out. My persistence paid off, as I was able to negotiate with them over the phone prior to planning a trip. I then jumped on a plane with my dad early on a Saturday morning, purchased the vehicle, and drove back home. We got back to Maryland by Sunday evening, and back to my full-time job on Monday morning. We stopped at a memorable Texas BBQ spot called Up in Smoke. It was some of the most delicious BBQ I have ever had. It was an exhausting trip physically,

but I was amped. No one knew a thing Monday morning when I returned to work, but I had to keep it a secret because I couldn't afford to lose my job just yet....

I had grand plans to go to the surf ranch in Austin, but it had shut down only a few weeks after opening due to a hole in the liner. This will certainly be in the plans, in the future. We saw herds of deer in Texarkana. Drove through Memphis in the middle of the night. I also desired to stop in Pisgah, but it was snowing in the mountains, so we decided to make our way home. None of this seemed to matter as I knew there would be another time. The journey was underway in building out the first mobile physical therapy studio, and I was amped!!!! Did I say that already?!?

After you choose a vehicle, comes the fun part. This was literally one of the most fun parts of the whole process for me, and that was actually building a "prototype" for the first mobile physical therapy studio. You probably picked this book up, because you are wondering how to do it, what materials you need, what kind of tools are necessary, and how much help you will need during the build out. Luckily I am going to tell you EVERYTHING as I want more dedicated practitioners on the road around the country providing the best possible care to their clients with a true client centered approach to their treatment.

After you purchase a vehicle you will want to build it out as quickly as possible, because you will have to begin making monthly payments on the vehicle. Keep in mind, this would be the same situation if you were renting a brick and mortar space, and needed to build it out into a physical therapy clinic for your brand. Fortunately, it is fairly cheap compared to the cost of renting a brick and mortar location. I purchased my Sprinter van for 56K, putting 10K down. My monthly payments are $645 per month. Sure if you were just starting out you could rent a space for cheaper, but your rent will just increase as you see more clients and need a larger space. With a mobile clinic you will have paid off your "rent" within 5-7 years at the most, and then costs will drastically decrease.

UPS, and FedEx use these vehicles for a reason, and that is because they are said to last up to 500,000 miles if properly maintained. Again, let me put that into perspective. The new normal for cars is at least 200,000 miles on average during its lifetime, and at an average of 15,000 miles per year, the vehicle would last at least 13 years. You will just pay for maintenance, and fuel for about half of the life of the vehicle.

You may also be wondering the cost of the build out. It did cost a lot of time, working weekends, and after work when I was still working my full-time job. Being the prototype, I also had to plan and figure out exactly what goes into the build out and the materials that would work best. Financially, the build out was approximately 20 grand give or take, which includes heat and AC for the treatment area, all the materials, and a custom functional trainer for workouts. Heat and AC are a necessity, and truly make it a studio on wheels providing comfort to you and your clients. It was the most costly purchase coming in at roughly 7K for air conditioning, a diesel fired heater, and an second battery installed under the hood. This could be done cheaper if you are able to do this part yourself. However, I did outsource this job to make it look professional. Also, with the heater tying into the diesel system and AC into the vehicle's current air conditioning system I wanted it not only to look professional, but done right. I needed a working electrical system, and to limit any potential hazards or risk.

Recommendations For You:

	2016 Sprinter Stock Super High	2019 Sprinter w/ 28" Cali Camper Top*	2019 Sprinter w/ 16" Aero Top	2020 Transit Stock High Roof: 148" Extended	2020 Transit w/ 30" Super Camper Top: 148" extended
Interior Height	~7'3"	~7'11"	~6'11"	~6'10"	~7'2"
Overall Vehicle Height	~9'8"	~10'4"	~9'4"	~9'2"	~9'5"
Wheel Base	170"	144"	144"	148"	148"
Overall Vehicle Length	~22'10"	~19'6"	~19'6"	~19'7"	~19'7"
Cargo Length	~14'10"	~11'1"	~11'1"	~12	~12
Cargo Width Max	~5'10"	~5'10"	~5'10"		
Cargo Width @ Wheel Base	~4'5"	~4'5"	~4'5"	~4'7"	~4.7"
Ground to Side Door Step In Height	20"	20.9"	20.9"		
Keiser	Modified	No	Modified	Modified	Modified
Gas/Diesel	Diesel	Diesel	Diesel	Gas	Gas
Stock/Top	Stock	Top	Top	Stock	Top
Stock Base Price		~40K before Top & packages	~40K before Top & packages	~40K	~40K before Top & packages

- All Require Add ons such as RV Prep Package: for dual batteries, stronger alternator, high idle, etc.
- Both offer 4x4: Transit ~ 5K extra, Sprinter ~8K extra

The chart above reviews key specifications of the Pioneer PT Prototype and other similar options. The Pioneer PT prototype was built on a stock 2016 Mercedes Sprinter with a super high roof and 170" wheelbase.

I love my van, but it is no longer in production, and we have to keep up with the changing times. Fortunately, there are other options out there. This may come down to personal preference, cost, and your ideal client. Really think about who you are going to see. Each vehicle has positives and negatives to each.

However, I would try to stay above the 7 foot mark if you are going to be working with adults, overhead athletes at end ranges, plan to do plyometrics in the studio, or work with individuals with greater height. If you live in a temperate climate this may not be an issue as you can always go outside, but yes, you can modify treatment and have someone squat, kneel, sit or lie down for certain overhead exercises in a shorter vehicle.

Being 6'3" myself, I can tell you that I value the interior height, making it feel spacious. I really dig the 144" wheelbase Sprinter with the 28" Cali camper top. I think it looks awesome, has a more than sufficient interior height, and should be easier to drive than the 170" wheelbase. If however, you will be working primarily with children, or shorter individuals, then you may strongly consider the stock Ford Transit with the high roof option purely for cost and ease of build without custom add ons.

Length is another consideration. You shouldn't have trouble fitting a massage table in front of the wheel well of an extended van on the drivers side wall, however, on the shorter 144" wheel base Sprinter it does not appear that a regulation length massage table will fit. This may require you to adjust the floor plan, and put the massage table over top of the wheel well on either wall as well as shifting the exercise equipment towards the front of the vehicle.

The fiberglass tops shown in the chart above are built by a company called Fiberine in California. These are their best options for vehicle height and are about 5K give or take for the top only. They manufacture to order and offer many different options including installation, shipping, windows, wood reinforcement, and clear coat finishing for an additional cost. I'd highly recommend the wood reinforcements and strips to make life easier if you plan to add a headliner.

If you do not have the ability to install a top yourself, Fiberine will do it, and if you don't live close it could be an opportunity for your own epic road trip. If this is not in your cards call your local van outfitters and get a quote. It requires cutting the factory roof off your van, bolting, screwing, and sealing the new fiberglass top down. You need a few strong dudes, or a fork lift to help position it into place.

There are a couple other considerations. First, these are approximate measurements. Second, I would also recommend that you consider the materials that use during the build out. Every material has a thickness to it, and will reduce the size of your space from the above specifications. For example, the interior height of the Pioneer PT prototype is ~7 feet after the thickness of insulation, headliner, lights, and flooring were included.

To Do List:

- Figure out who your audience is
- Decide what you need in your mobile studio
- Strongly consider design - see chapter 1: Floor Plan
- Pick the best vehicle to suite your needs
- Determine what assistance is necessary & who can assist

Materials & Tools Needed:

You will need a decent amount of tools and workspace to be able to complete this project. Preferably under cover so that you are able to complete the work even when the weather is not cooperating. A garage or workshop would be perfect or at least having your workspace adjacent to the van. During this project I used my parent's garage and parked the van outside in the driveway. I purchased most of the materials from Home Depot or Lowe's. One or two things from Ace Hardware, and the RV panels from a local RV store and repair shop. Fortunately I have access to these tools, but if you do not own them or have a family member with them, there are ways to access or rent them. Many communities like Baltimore, may have community garages or manufacturing centers that will allow you access to these tools. Otherwise, Home Depot and Ace Hardware both rent tools as well.

Materials:

- 3M High Strength Adhesive Spray 90 - Green Bottle
- 3M Thinsulate SM600L Acoustic Thermal Auto insulation (~70 linear feet for 170 WB)
- Self tapping sheet metal screws- Various lengths: don't pierce through vehicle
- Bead board/ Wainscoting/ RV Vinyl Wall Material
- Construction Adhesive- (Liquid Nails- heavy duty)

- Silicone adhesive- (For fiberglass)
- Oak/ Maple/ Birch Plywood for Cabinets
- Wood Glue
- 2x4's (6-8)
- Stain/Paint
- Rivets
- Automotive Grommets- to be used on sliding door and panels rear doors to hold vinyl RV panels in place

What tools will you need:

- Tape Measure
- Square
- Large Sharp Scissors
- Razor Blade
- Pen/ Pencil/ Marker/ Caulk Line
- Jig Saw/ Table Saw/ Circular Saw
- Miter Saw
- Palm Sander/ Belt Sander
- Screw Gun/ Nail Gun
- Hammer
- Putty Knife
- Caulking Gun
- Paint Brush/ Paint Rollers
- Riveter
- Hemming tool, bending seamer, or sheet metal brake (borrow/rent)
- Wood plane

- Pen/Pencil
- Rags
- Wrench- Torx bits
- Imagination/ Patience/ Hard-work

Step 1: Floor Plan

Designing the floor plan or layout for your mobile studio is your first step, and should be fun as it is the start of a new chapter in your life as you begin down a new path into owning your own mobile health and wellness practice.

I am a huge fan of design and vision so this step made me excited for what was to come. I could envision seeing client's in this space, and you should too. You can make this how you want so that it best serves your clients. I liked the idea of having a treatment area and an exercise area. I recommend sketching a few designs and determining what works best for you.

After quite a few designs, I settled on putting the exercise area is in the back of the vehicle near the back doors. This is in the open area adjacent to the functional trainer behind the wheel wells. Cabinets were built over top of the wheel wells primarily for storage. However, they serve a secondary purpose in that a client can hold onto them for safety and balance exercises with various levels of assistance. This helps to break up the space into different areas. Then the "treatment area" with the massage table is located on the wall as soon as you step into the vehicle. On the right as you step in are the front seats. The passenger seat has the ability to swivel 180 degrees to turn around and face backwards, which is key to preserving space, and creating more seating. It works great as a a seating option for a family member, parent, or even your client when performing your evaluation. It is a fantastic option that helps to avoid more stuff that requires to be tied down while the vehicle is in motion.

One thing to note is that the swivel for the passenger seat does add increased height to the seat. For those clients who are shorter in height, their feet will no longer touch the ground, and may be uncomfortable if they have lower back or extremity pain. You may want to consider a small step stool for support, which can double down as a piece of exercise equipment.

To Do List:

- Sketch a few different designs. (graph paper helps for scale)
- Determine what works best for the clients you serve
- Determine what you want to put in the vehicle (storage, sink, equipment, LEDs, machine/air compressor, etc.)
- Determine where you will put your massage table
- Determine what exercise equipment is necessary for your practice
- Finalize a design choice and dive in

Step 2: Heat and AC

Heat and air-conditioning are a must in Maryland, so I had both installed in the treatment area for client comfort. How is the weather in your state?

The heater is amazing. It is a Webasto Air Top 2000 STC, and it takes a small drip of fuel from the tank, even when the engine is off, to burn and produce plenty of heat for the treatment area. This makes the space comfortable even on the coldest days, and there is no need to run the engine. Maryland gets down into the single digits, sometimes close to 0, and I never have to turn the heater all the way up when working with a client. Another popular diesel fired heater option is Espar.

If you chose to go with a Ford Transit, be mindful of the type of engine. Ford did offer a diesel engine in the past, but the 2020 Ford Transit line, now only offers gas powered engines. Webasto does offer a gas powered heater option as well.

As per the owner's manual, the Webasto requires no periodic maintenance. However, they do recommend a visual inspection prior to the heating season by an authorized Webasto Sales & Service Center to ensure that all components are free from damage and in proper working condition. It is also recommended that the heater be run for a minimum of 5-10 minutes each month, even during the warmer months when it is not required, so that a clean, fresh supply of fuel is kept in the heater's fuel system, and all moving parts are in top operating condition.

I have since read online forums that Espar may be slightly more reliable for diesel powered air heaters. During my first build out, I had not yet realized that another company makes diesel fired air heaters for a Sprinter van. My suggestion is that you go to both Webasto and Eberspaecher's (Espar) website, and locate a dealer that is in your area. If you have both in your area, contact each and get a quote. However, it is nice to have an authorized dealer in your area not only for installation, but also in case there is a maintenance issue does arise down the road.

The air conditioner I had installed is also Webasto. It is a Vancouver model, horizontal cooling evaporator unit, and it is mounted above the driver and passenger seat in the storage area facing backwards towards the treatment area. This does require that the engine be turned on.

When a vehicle is left running it is recommended by Mercedes to run the vehicle at high idle. This is an added option that Mercedes offers for campers and also service vehicles that make regular stops and sit idling for any length of time during delivery. High idle is recommended by the manufacturer to burn carbon and prevent it from accumulating in the engine. Both Ford and Mercedes offer packages such as an RV prep package that can save you from some headaches including dual batteries, a stronger alternator, and the high idle option.

The auxiliary or second battery is a must. This battery will give you power for your LED lights, and any other object that requires power. It can even assist your starter battery to start the vehicle. In my case the auxiliary battery also powers the water pump at my sink, and air compressor for the functional trainer. The auxiliary battery gets charged back up when the engine is running. In my experience it returns to full charge during my drive time between clients, and on the commute home at the end of the day.

I had the second battery mounted under the hood on the driver's side in a special battery tray made by Mercedes for Sprinters. There is also an option to mount the battery underneath the vehicle via a battery box. Batteries can be installed underneath the seats as well, but you have to have a proper ventilation system for the battery.

Keep in mind this auxiliary battery is primarily meant to facilitate the starter battery, by preventing it from draining and dying while the vehicle is off. It is not meant to power a 12v refrigerator or power any device for an extended period of time that draws excessive Amps. The second battery is wired and tied into your vehicle's existing electrical system that is mounted underneath the driver's seat.

There are videos online that will help you self install to save money if you feel comfortable with this undertaking. Due to the diesel fired heater being installed into the fuel system, and the integration into the vehicle's AC system, I found that for me it was best to outsource the installation of the heat and AC. This would ensure that it came out looking professional and was done correctly. Know your limitations, and what tasks you feel comfortable undertaking.

To Do List:

- Determine your needs for the weather in your area
- Secure a professional or dealer that can install AC/Heat/Auxiliary battery for you
- Be patient, as this step did take time

Step 3: Insulation

There are different options here, but you need something flexible. I actually chose 3M Thinsulate, and ordered a large roll of ~70 feet. 70 feet sufficiently insulates a 170 inch wheelbase super high roof Mercedes Sprinter Van. A Ford

Transit extended version will be close, and 144 inch wheelbase Mercedes Sprinter will only require ~50 foot roll. Thinsulate has an R value of 5.2. The R value was rather high compared to other options creating greater insulation and sound deadening effects. It is also flexible, which makes it easy to work with, which is key during the installation process.

I will go through my thought process with you on my decision. Thinsulate has both insulation, and sound deadening properties as well as allowing moisture to pass through the material, not trapping it between the wall of the van and then insulation. The hydrophobic properties were important so that water or humidity are not absorbed like the classic pink fiberglass or denim insulation that can be purchased at Home Depot or Lowe's.

All insulation has been rated at different "R" values that designate thickness and cold ratings, but fiberglass and denim collect moisture and can create moldy smells and even rust the shell of the vehicle in more humid environments or in the case of an accident. Remember, even working out and breathing hard when exercising causes water vapor from your breath and sweat to be created. This is why many camper vans have built in vents with fans. The foam boarding is an option, but impossible to cut into all of the irregular holes in the frame of the van. These holes are various sizes and depths that would make this job a nightmare and not allow you to fully insulate all the cracks and crevices properly.

The other option is a spray in closed cell foam, which is more expensive than Thinsulate, and can be really messy. Foam spray is typically outsourced, because there is potential to trap water vapor behind the foam spray. Again, this will cause your vehicle to rust out if it is done incorrectly.

3M Thinsulate is the same material used in winter jackets and gloves. It is used in many vehicles for the sound deadening and insulation properties. It comes in a large roll and can be cut into any shape with a sharp pair of scissors. Then, it can be glued to the walls and ceiling with 3M adhesive Hi-strength 90 spray. Be patient when using this spray. Make sure to spray in an open area and wait until the glue becomes tacky before attempting to put the insulation up on the walls. If you attempt to put it up too early when the glue is still wet, the Thinsulate will not stick properly and fall off. For smaller spots the adhesive spray is not necessary and small pieces can be stuffed into the cracks. Thinsulate has a 5.2 R value. You may consider doubling up in certain areas where there is adequate space. You can double up that material as long as you are not compressing it. Compression of the Thinsulate negates the insulation and sound deadening properties. This would be recommended in environments with extreme heat or cold, as well as helping to make your vehicle a quieter ride. The change in road noise is very noticeable with insulation installed. Your van will go from sounding like a tin can when driving, to a much quieter ride. Another tip, I recommend cutting the Thinsulate over a couple days because it ends up being a lot on your hands. Make sure your scissors are sharp, and be patient!

The one area that I did use rigid foam insulation was for the floor of the vehicle. I believe it was ¼ inch thickness. I took up the stock flooring by taking out the Torx bolts, and then traced the stock flooring onto the rigid foam insulation that I purchased. I cut the insulation and pieced it together into the shape of the floor. Then, I duct taped it together, and laid the foam insulation down. Then, I put the stock flooring back on top, and bolted it back into place.

To Do List:

- Determine how much Thinsulate is required for your van
- Purchase 3M Thinsulate (70' roll for 170" WB & 50' roll for 144"WB)
- Purchase 3-5 cans of 3M adhesive Hi- strength 90 spray (you will need this later too, but keep receipt, because you can always return what you don't use)
- Purchase a proper pair of large scissors if you do not already own them.

Step 4: Electrical

Electrical is next. You must run your wires before closing in the walls. Wires are not be connected yet, but run roughly into place. Different thickness wires are required for safety depending on the devices you chose. It may be best to consult an electrician after you dial in the exact lights and devices that you need.

Wiring will be run from the auxiliary battery to your devices. I always like to keep it clean and simple so I only have a few devices that require electric. The lights, the water pump, and the air compressor. For overhead lighting I chose 4 LED lights, as LEDs are the most efficient and use very little wattage. These 4 LEDs are able to light then entire interior of the studio to make it feel like daylight. Electric is used for a water pump for clean water use at a sink for proper sanitation. Lastly, electric was utilized to run the air compressor for the performance trainer. Each of these devices has a switch to turn on and off as needed. That was it! I did institute one small trick to be able to control 2 lights at a time so the LEDs can be turned off above the treatment table when necessary to help create a relaxing vibe and take it easy on client's retinas when they are lying supine.

I kept it simple because I did not want to deal with a generator. Generators can be noisy. Who wants to hear the constant hum of a generator? Not me, nor my clients. Instead they can listen to music or have a conversation in peace. The plus side of generators is that they do create more power to run larger devices. This could be useful at events, workshops, or potentially your daily practice. I do not utilize a high low table, electric stimulation, or ultrasound as part of my practice. Electric stimulation only provides temporary relief, which I find a waste of time as I can achieve better pain relief with manual techniques. It also wastes valuable time, when you need to get to your next client. But, you could always utilize a portable TENS/NMES unit instead and even lend it to clients on a case by case basis. Ultrasound does not have great evidence other than for tendinosis in combination with other therapies such as eccentric strengthening. For me the benefits definitely do not outweigh the negatives. As a massage therapist, you may want warm towels or a heated blanket? These are all decisions that you will have to make.

You do have to be aware of compatibility issues when it comes to electric. First, you will not have a normal outlet to plug typical household devices into in the mobile studio, it must be a 12v compatible device unless you have an inverter. If you have an inverter then you would be able to plug in a normal 120v household plug. An inverter must have a power source through a battery, battery bank, solar, or some combination. This means being able to plug devices into a cigarette lighter, which is 12v or a USB plug are going to be the easiest.

Solar power may be beneficial for those of you who live in sunny states, but there were too many drawbacks for me in Maryland. I am using the vehicle as a mobile physical therapy studio, not an outdoor adventure vehicle where I am living off the grid for days at a time. First, the expense of going solar, and second added height were huge issues. The height of the vehicle is already "super high", and it would be very prone to damage if there is additional height added to the roof from solar panels mounted on top. Side streets, client's driveways, and parking already require a vigilant eye to avoid small branches from hitting the roof of the truck. Solar panels will also reduce aerodynamics and gas milage with the additional height.

An extra USB port in the treatment area for clients to charge their phones has come into handy as well. This has come in handy not only for my clients, but also for myself during treatment sessions and has even spurred conversations at events where someones phone was dying and needed a charge.

You may be wondering about the exercise equipment. The stock performance trainer does require a normal household 120v plug, but there is another way. There is always another way. The on-board air compressor that I installed, it does not require a 120v plug. I purchased an air compressor specifically for trucks with 12v that ties into the system. This is strong enough to run the performance trainer, and even fill up my tires when they are low. I will go into more details in step #12 on the exercise equipment.

To Do List:

- Determine what electrical devices you need
- Determine if you can purchase these in 12V

If they are not 12V, how will you convert or power this device? (ex. generator/inverter)

- Purchase LED lighting sufficient for space
- Secure electrician to perform the job or materials you need

Step 5: Framing

When you begin to get the framing for the walls installed, you can start to envision the van becoming a mobile studio for your clients. It is a huge step that starts to bring everything together.

There are multiple ways to do this, but I will explain how I did it, and my reasoning. Originally I wanted to use lumber to create a rugged, unfinished look just staining the wood, but ended up going a different route. Instead I chose materials that would maintain the maximum amount of width in the vehicle, allowing the largest amount of space. These materials would even help to save money. They help to cut cost, because they are both cheaper to purchase, and also lighter weight, which helps to reduce fuel costs. Higher payload causes more fuel consumption. These materials are also flexible enough to conform to the curvature of the walls of the van.

Unless you look closely, you may not realize, but the walls curve from front to back and from top to bottom of the vehicle. The material that you choose must be flexible enough to conform to the walls for mounting, and to conserve space.

I used two layers of material for the side walls. In this step I used ⅛ inch hardboard to close in the insulation. This created a surface area to adhere the outer walls to for a finished look. I wanted it to look clean without a lot of fasteners visible.

You must purchase the correct screws that are self tapping sheet metal screws, and the correct length not to puncture the outer shell of the vehicle. We used ⅜ and ¼ inch self tapping sheet metal screws depending on the thickness of the material and the amount of space available in the structure of the van to adhere to. Do not use screws that are too long!

First, you must look at the lines in the vehicle as to where the frame points are that create strength in the walls. If you look approximately 3 feet up from the floor there is a straight line that runs from the front to the back of the vehicle offering a spot to adhere self tapping screws into the frame of the vehicle.

It is helpful to create templates out of cardboard or a large paper roll to trace onto the hardboard to cut out later with a jig saw. I would recommend to cut the templates to the exact size and tape them up on the walls to ensure they fit together as you hope. Again, measure as many times as you need and take precautions with the templates so you do not waste material. Pieces from one side of the vehicle can be recycled and utilized on the opposite side. This means that the driver's side and passenger side of the vehicle have some common cuts that are mirror images of each other. Be patient and you will get the hang of things as you go.

Also, this is super important and will save you time and work later. Read this paragraph in its entirety. Once the hardboard pieces are all cut test these together before screwing them into the frame by putting them into place. Once complete and fitting well, use the hardboard as templates for your finishing walls (Step 7) especially if you used paper cut outs. The hardboard is much more exact and easier to trace onto the outer finishing walls. This is most useful for the corner cuts where the inside walls of the van are curved.

<u>To Do List:</u>

- Determine how you will build your framing
- Purchase the material you will use for walls

- Secure tools including tape measure, Jigsaw, screw gun, self tapping screws
- Secure cardboard to use for templates to trace pattern on the hardboard
- Plan everything out!

Step 6: Storage

Next up is storage, or in my case the cabinets. How do you want your storage designed? What do you want the storage compartments to hold? What type of door or locking mechanism will you use? Cabinets are crucial to prevent your stuff from flying around the mobile studio when you are driving down the road. This is why I chose 2 specific types of cabinets so that my stuff stays secure and in one place.

I used large sliding bypass doors for one cabinet. This cabinet is the sink, and stores 2 large 5 gallon water jugs. One jug is just for clean water, and the other is for dirty water. There is a pump mounted in this cabinet as well as storage for various other products such as massage cream, cleaning supplies, cups for myofascial decompression, weights, etc. The pump brings water from the fresh water jug to the faucet for hand washing, and then the drain leads directly into the dirty water jug where it can later be dumped.

The other cabinet on the opposite side of the cabin is used for a trash can, a dirty laundry bin, with access from the top, and sliding drawers below. The drawers lock into place when closed and store assessment tools, tape, scissors, pens, my license, and even papers that I use during my evaluation and sales process. These drawers are an easy location to find things quickly.

The water is stored inside the vehicle, because I live in an area where temperatures freeze at nighttime during the colder months of the year. The water is much less likely to freeze inside the vehicle rather than mounted underneath the vehicle. I still have to drain the water jugs completely for a period of time in the middle of winter to avoid freezing overnight. During this time of the year I stick to hand sanitizer, and coffee stops to wash my hands. However, if you live in a temperate climate, you may consider mounting the water underneath the vehicle to save a ton of space. Space is valuable! There are grommets built into the Sprinter where you can run tubing or wiring from underneath the vehicle to inside and vise versa without drilling a hole in the floor.

Where did I build these cabinets? I built these cabinets over top of the wheel wells for multiple reasons. First, there was already a wheel well in the way, and it made sense to built up over top of it.

Second, it created increased weight over the rear wheels. It is a rear wheel drive van, and you want more weight in the back to prevent the wheels from spinning on wet roads or during snowy conditions. Think of it like a pick up truck. In the winter time, people put snow or salt in the back of their truck to maintain traction while driving. The same is true for a van. All the weight is up front under the hood with the weight of the engine, but unless it is loaded in the back, there is minimal weight in the rear of the vehicle to keep the wheels down on the road. We need more junk in the trunk!

Third, I built the cabinets over the wheel wells to create a "workout" area in the rear of the mobile studio where I mounted the functional trainer in the center rear of the vehicle just in front of the rear doors. It separated the "treatment" area from the "workout" area in a way designating different spaces within the studio.

The Ford Transit vans are front wheel drive, so weight in the back of the vehicle does it apply to the same degree.

How did I do it? The cabinets were stick built. This means that each piece of the frame of the cabinet were cut and framed by hand. It was framed out from the ground up. There were some major considerations during this part of the build. How big will the water jugs be, and what shape will best fit here? What kind of trash cans or bins will I utilize for the trash can and the dirty laundry on the other side? I wanted to maintain the most amount of space that I possibly could in the width of the vehicle between wheel wells, but also needed to be able to fit all the essentials to provide an excellent treatment. I would suggest taking a lot of measurements during the process. The old saying goes, "measure twice, cut once," truly comes in handy here. You may also want to research and purchase the water jugs and trash cans prior to building this out to ensure that everything will fit as expected.

First, I chose to put the sink with the water pump and water jugs on the driver's side due to the requirement for electric to run the water pump. It was easier, because it was not necessary to run wiring over to the passenger side of the vehicle. That helped to make that decision fairly straight forward.

Then, it was time to build out a platform over top of the wheel wells on both sides of the vehicle creating a strong supportive base for the cabinets. I used ¾ inch plywood for the base that ran horizontally and level just over the wheel wells. By stick building up with a cabinet in mind, the frame for the cabinets were created. I used both screws and wood glue to help hold everything secure. Once the frame was built, then I used ⅛ inch birch plywood to create the sides to the cabinets, and also the sliding doors for the cabinet on the driver's side for the sink. The sliding doors work well, because they are snug and do not fly open when driving, and they also allow accessibility for large objects such as the water jugs.

To Do List:

- Determine what space is necessary for storage
- Determine if you require running water

- Determine where you will put your portable massage table
- Secure plywood and lumber to use to stick build cabinet
- Secure cardboard to assist with templates
- Secure proper tools: saws, tape measure, pencil, screw gun, screws, wood glue

Step 7: Headliner

The headliner was an interesting undertaking, and quite possibly the most difficult to figure out the correct materials. I am sure there are other ways, and a professional may be able to assist, but this is what I did and it is holding up well after 2 years into practice.

If you are able to go with a stock Ford Transit with a high roof, then this step will be similar to the walls as you can adhere self tapping sheet metal screws into the frame to create a finished ceiling. If not, and your ideal client requires a higher ceiling then you may consider the option below.

What made this decision so difficult for me was that the roof on the super high version of the Sprinter van is fiberglass instead of steel or aluminum alloy. It is also curved significantly side to side and front to back. This made any type of wood very difficult to conform to the ceiling of the vehicle to create a finished look, and difficult to secure to the ceiling. This is why I chose a headliner to complete the job.

As always my first goal was to maximize overhead space. I wanted to put a headliner in that was light in weight and that cover the insulation on the ceiling to give it a finished more professional look. I also wanted to be able to mount LED lighting overhead. I decided to use lightweight waterproof and water resistant materials.

The materials that I utilized were a very thin all weather carpeting that was tan in color to mimic a fabric. This material is resistant to humidity, and water vapor in the vehicle from working out as well as hot humid days. The all weather carpeting was mounted on corrugated plastic cardboard or Coroplast with 90 grade 3M spray adhesive. Coroplast was chosen, because it is a lightweight material that is waterproof, and flexible enough to conform to the curvature in the ceiling. This was the only material that could conform to the shape of the roof. Prior to gluing the materials together, carefully read below.

First, measure the exact dimensions that are necessary to fit a piece of Coroplast up onto the ceiling along the fiberglass ribbing on the roof. It helps to make a template. Take your time and measure carefully! Make sure you have enough room to fit the adjacent piece so that there is a location to adhere the headliner to. The 2016 Sprinter with the super high roof has fiberglass reinforcements running horizontally every few feet. I measured halfway onto the horizontal reinforcements on the ceiling so that each adjacent piece could fit securely.

Then, I took approximately a half inch off those measurements in both length and width to accommodate the thickness of the carpeting to be mounted on top of the Coroplast. The all weather carpeting is ~¼ inch thick, and wraps around the edges of the Coroplast on all sides. By adding a ¼ inch on both sides that equals the ½ that must be considered to fit properly when mounted. The Coroplast was cut with a razor, and fit into place to make sure it fits.

Next, I decided where the LED lighting would be mounted on the ceiling, and attached a small piece of ¼ inch plywood onto the Coroplast with the 90 grade 3M spray adhesive before covering it with the all weather carpeting. Drill a large hole through the plywood and Chloroplast so that the wiring for the LED lights can be fed through.

Finally the all weather carpeting was adhered to the Coroplast. Take adequate time for the glue to become tacky before applying the carpeting. If you do not wait long enough, then the carpeting will begin to fall off the Coroplast, and will sag when applied to the ceiling. This is not the look you are going for. You may want to utilize a roller to ensure the materials are stuck together firmly. Again, with assistance we fit each piece, one at a time, into place to ensure a proper fit.

Then, silicone caulking was applied to the reinforcements on the ceiling and the pieces were pressed into place. This silicone caulking was specifically designed to adhere material to fiberglass and withstand high heat.

Have about six, 2x4s ready to create a brace that can be cut to the appropriate length, and fit into place to support the headliner while the glue dries. These can be sitting across the vehicle from the floor on one side to the roof on the opposite side forming a crossing pattern like an "X" or a "T" that helps to provide temporary support so that you do not have to stand there holding everything is place for 24 hours until the adhesive is completely dry. Be sure to place a flat piece of wood or towel on the end to avoid leaving indentations in the headliner. It should be snug to hold things in place and secure overnight for the adhesive to fully dry without deforming the material.

To Do List:

- Decide what material you will use
- Decide how you will hang your lights
- Secure ~6: 2x4 that can support the headline while adhesive dries
- Secure correct amount of Corrugated plastic/ Coroplast- It can be purchased at Home Depot

- Secure fabric, material from convertible repair shop, or thin all weather carpeting for the headliner
- Secure LED lighting for treatment area
- Find 4 pieces of scrap plywood from your cabinets
- Secure 90 grade 3M Adhesive and Heat resistant adhesive (It gets hot in vehicles in the summer sun)
- Have a friend or family member assist with this job

Step 8: Walls

This step is optional if you chose to use lumber in step 4 - Walls, but I will explain how I chose to complete this task and maintain maximum width in the studio.

I did things differently to create a finished professional look with wainscoting on the bottom 3 feet, and vinyl RV panels on the top. I kept the wainscoting white, and painted the top a sky blue to go along with the color scheme of my logo. I am still looking for the right person, but the goal is to have an artist paint my logo and a landscape on the wall.

The wainscoting was cut to stop halfway into the horizontal straight line of framing that was previously mentioned, so it could be tacked in securely at the top of the wainscoting, but also leave space to tack in the bottom of the vinyl RV panels to the top of the wall. ***See picture above***

By taking exact measurements previously for the hard board, this step will not be as time consuming. Use the hardboard as templates and trace the shape onto the back of your finishing walls. Then cut out finishing walls with a jigsaw for the curved portions, and a table saw or circular saw for the straight lines of the cut. Double check a good fit and make necessary tweaks. The cut doesn't have to be perfect, but should fit close. If there is a slight gap this is okay, as you will want to add finish work, such as molding to complete the project. This is also a time that you will want to measure well and cut holes for lighting and electric into your walls. The Sprinter comes with stock lighting on the walls that I kept, as these lights come on when the doors open, and it also helps to provide extra light in the rear of the vehicle. Measure twice, cut once. Drilling a hole into the vinyl wall, and then using a jigsaw to cut out the holes for the stock lighting was the easiest way.

At this time I also purchased LED lights online to fit into the stock lighting on the wall, to keep energy use down, improve brightness, and also decrease the risk of fire. These are the lights that turn on when you open the doors of the vehicle. The stock light bulbs create a ton of heat and could potentially create a fire risk. Be careful the stock bulbs get very hot! Most LEDs are cool to the touch and will improve safety. Still be sure to keep the space clear behind the lights, making sure you did not stuff it with insulation. You can also create a backing to the light for greater protection. To find out what type of LED light you need, take out the stock bulbs when cool, and read specifications. Then purchase small LED bulbs online.

Then, comes another big step towards creating a finished product, paint. Paint the vinyl RV walls the color you wish with 2 coats of paint, and allow them to dry. You should consider what color best creates the environment you hope to accomplish for your ideal client. This will vary, but is important. I chose a sky blue that is in my logo color scheme. Blue symbolizes trust, loyalty, wisdom, confidence, intelligence, faith, and truth. You may choose the color green for life, renewal, fertility, or yellow for happiness, positivity, and energy. This is up to you, and how you want your mobile studio to FEEL.

Once again, ensure a good fit, and then apply construction adhesive to the back and fit the pieces into place. I utilized heavy duty Liquid Nails, because this type of construction adhesive is heat resistant. Cars get very hot in the summer's sun, and the adhesive must be able to sustain high heat levels, or else your walls will just fall down. The interior of a car can elevate above 170 degrees Fahrenheit in the summer's sun. These were tacked in to help hold them in place, and then secured with spare 2x4 pieces cut as cross members to hold the walls firmly in place while the construction adhesive sets. Please use rags and also spare pieces of left over hardboard at the end of your 2x4s so that you do not damage your vinyl RV walls. You may have to do some touch up painting once everything is complete.

To Do List:

- Purchase wall material- I used Wainscoting from Home Depot and Vinyl RV paneling from the local RV repair shop and store.
- Purchase small LED bulbs for walls
- Purchase construction adhesive- Heavy Duty Liquid Nails
- Secure proper tools- jig saw, saws, rags, tape measure, nail gun?
- Determine wall color and the feel you desire for your mobile studio

Step 9: Electrical Chase

I wanted a finished look, without electrical wires hanging out in plain view on the wall of the drivers side of the vehicle. First, I used zip ties to secure the electrical wiring together and to the frame of the vehicle, just below the headliner. The wires begin in the driver's seat, then run up inside the roll bar, and down the driver's side of the vehicle to reach the LED lighting, and the switches mounted in the back of the vehicle on the driver's side wall. I decided to use tin flashing covered with left over all weather carpeting to blend it into the headliners. The tin flashing was utilized to help prevent fire if something were to malfunction with the electrical work. It also provides accessibility.

Depending on the wall material you utilize you may be able to use a different material for the wiring, but keep in mind the curvature of the vehicle from front to back. It needs to be flexible.

Be very careful with the tin flashing as it is sharp and can cut your hands. Please use sturdy gloves to prevent injury. You do not want to hurt your money makers. Snips were used to cut the flashing as needed. Then, I used the 3M hi-strength 90 adhesive spray to attach the all weather carpeting to the tin flashing to help it match the headliner. With assistance to help hold things level, and in place, I riveted the tin flashing together, and screwed it into the frame with self tapping screws. Be careful not to use screws that are too long, as you do not want to pierce the exterior of the vehicle. This will cause rust, and water damage due to leaks.

The tin flashing was screwed in on the bottom, bent to form a conduit or wire chase, and then tucked in and tied secure on the top. By tying in the top rather than screwing it into place it helps allow greater ease of access if need be. A hemming tool, bending seamer, or even a sheet metal brake come into handy here. If you are friends with a builder or more specifically a roofer they should have these tools and potentially be able to help if you are unsure.

To Do List:

- Secure a roll of tin flashing, snips, riveter, rivets, carpet, self tapping screws, zip ties, hammer
- Secure protective gloves
- Secure tool necessary to bend tin flashing- hemming tool, bending seamer, or sheet metal brake
- Get assistance for hanging and securing
- Be careful with your moneymakers!

Step 10: Flooring

Each step creates more and more excitement as you move one step closer to your dreams of a mobile studio and the freedom it will bring with it to you, your family, and your business. This is certainly one of those exciting steps.

For flooring I wanted a finished look, and the current flooring in the vehicle did not appear to have long term durability. I ended up going with a vinyl flooring for numerous reasons. It is durable, water resistant, easy to clean, easy to install, and I could find a material with some texture or grip to it. I wanted something that would not be slippery if people would come into the mobile studio during the rain or had slippery shoes. Vinyl flooring is also meant to float freely so you do not have to worry about nailing it down or using adhesive to secure the flooring in place. Another advantage is that it can expand and contract with the weather.

Vinyl flooring is easy to install these days, clicking into place, making this a relatively easy task. Just ensure that the measurements are correct and use a circular saw and jigsaw to cut the material. Also, be sure to leave about a ¼ inch or so around the edge next to the walls. Depending on the time of year that you are installing the flooring, this material will expand and contract depending on temperature, expanding when it is hot, and contracting when it is cold. Be sure to leave slight space so your flooring does not bubble up in the hot sun especially if this portion of the project is completed on a cooler day.

The only thing that made this part difficult was the anchors on the floor. I wanted to keep the anchors exposed on the floor so that I could have a place to bungee or tie down objects securely while I am driving around between appointments. This is super important because you need to be able to tie down the treatment table, and stool at the very least, but potentially equipment as well. It has also come into handy with tables for events, and even mountain bikes during transport. As always, measure as best you can, and use a jigsaw for this task to cut out the shape of the floor anchors. These anchors will also hold portions of the floor in place, which is a blessing and a curse when the material expands and contracts with the change in temperatures. Tighten it down firm, but not as tight as you can make it, because the flooring will bend and not latch together properly.

This leads into step 10, but you will want to do this now. You will want to create a finished look at the back and the entrance on the side of the mobile studio via the sliding door. Stair nosing is a perfect choice for this task. This also helps to hold the flooring into place. I used a strip of 1x1 inch maple material that was left over and mitered down on one corner to fit over the edge of the flooring, and screwed into place. It may be just as easy to purchase stair nosing for a durable edge to help secure your flooring in place. You are almost done, great job so far!

To Do List:

- Determine material to suite your needs
- Purchase flooring
- Purchase or make stair nosing
- Secure proper tools- tape measure, jig saw, saws, wrench, Torx

Step 11: Finish Work

Wow! What a build. Things are really coming together and you can now envision seeing clients in the mobile studio wherever your ideal client needs it most. Trim work is important to completing the project. I used molding around the base where the floor meets the walls, and also a "chair rail" molding to cover the gap between the wainscoting and the vinyl RV walls. My brand and preference is a natural look, so I used stain for a lot of these pieces. They were tacked in with a ⅜ inch brad gun, and glued in place with heavy duty Liquid Nails construction adhesive. I also covered the corners of the cabinets with molding to remove any sharp edges and create a finished look.

The sink is optional, as you can always use hand sanitizer and go into an establishment such as a gas station or a coffee shop, but I wanted the ease of everything onsite. The sink top was a tough decision. I thought about purchasing a piece of left-over granite from a kitchen store, but ended up using a nice piece of maple to continue with the natural theme and brand of my business, Pioneer PT. Wood was cheaper and something that I could do myself. With this piece, again measure exactly where you want the sink to sit and the faucet to be before cutting so you do not waste material. Wood was also a good choice, because the back had to be scribed or shaved down to fit the contours of the wall. The curvature in the vehicle from front to back caused this not to be a square cut. Use a wood plane for this task to shave the ends down.

First pencil in the approximate shape of the sink, potentially on the smaller side at first as you can always take more material off, but cannot put it back on. Then drill a hole through the material, and use a jigsaw to cut out the oval shape for the sink to sit in. Use a file to smooth the edges. Once it fits exactly how you want to, determine where the faucet hole should be drilled to drop the water towards the middle of the sink basin and drill the hole. I took this beautiful piece of wood and stained it a few times to the shade I desired. Then, I applied a polyurethane layer, sanded it, polyurethane, sanded, polyurethane it at least a handful of times to bring the wood alive and protect it from water droplets from the sink. I still utilize a hand towel to wipe up any excess water after washing my hands to maintain the integrity and cleanliness of the material.

At this point, the electrical work can be completed where everything is tied together from the switches to the lights, to the water pump for your sink, and the air compressor. Fortunately, we pre ran the wires earlier in the build, and we just had to get an electrician to connect everything together appropriately.

To Do List:

- Purchase material for trim work
- Purchase paint or stain
- Secure proper tools- tape measure, saws, construction adhesive/wood glue, rags, pencil, wood plane
- Secure electrician to complete electrical work

Step 12: Exercise Equipment

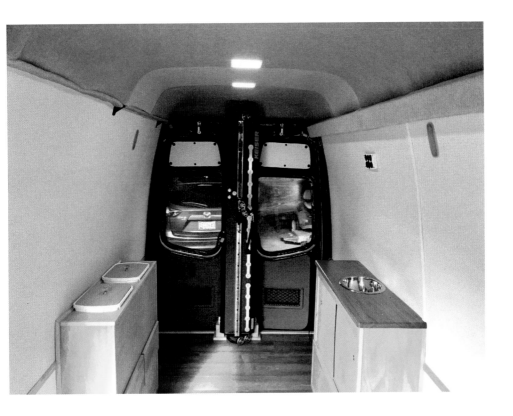

As with the rest of this prototype build for the first mobile physical therapy studio in the country I wanted to make it legitimate.   Yes, you can absolutely use resistance bands, at a fraction of the cost. However, I did my best to think from a client's point of view. Even though, both you and I know that you can get an amazing workout with minimal to no equipment there is something about equipment that makes it legitimate to customers. During my career I have been asked numerous times from potential clients, "Don't you need exercise equipment to get stronger." The choice is yours, but I will tell you what I did.

I wanted the one best piece of equipment possible, and this is why I chose a functional trainer. It has a clean and simple vibe without a lot of clutter or equipment that need to be tied down while in motion. I also went with the Keiser performance trainer due to its versatility to train different body parts in sport specific fashion. It is much more versatile than any weight stack due to the increments at a tenth of a pound from compressed air. This allows you to track progress and push clients forward each visit in an objective way. The only thing I had to figure out was how would I fit this in the mobile studio, how would I mount this securely, and how do I hook up the air compressor?

The machine can be purchased with a Keiser air compressor, but this requires a normal 120V plug that can be found in your home. This is the typical plug that can be found in the home in the United States. You can do this, but it would require a generator or portable power station. I chose against a generator because of the noise. Have you ever been to an outdoor festival or event such as the state or county fair and heard the generators buzzing? Even the most quiet can be annoying, and you have to find a place to store this when driving around. There are portable power stations that have popped up on the market over the past couple years, but I am not sure that they can support the Keiser air compressor.

Instead, I chose to purchase an on board air system that is compatible with the 12V power source typical in vehicles. It is an on board air compressor meant to be installed in vehicles and typically utilized for air horns or off-road vehicles that deflate their tires for rough terrain. For example; deflating tires for driving on the beach or certain uneven terrain to improve grip when off roading is common. Using an on board air compressor to pump your tires back up when you return to the paved road sends you on your way.

I purchased a medium duty Viair on board air system that fit the bill perfectly. It runs at max output of 150 PSI so it is recommended to replace the pressure switch that comes with the kit with a pressure switch that operates between 90-100 PSI so you do not harm the Keiser performance trainer. You can run this system off of your truck battery, but you should have your truck running while the compressors are on. Alternatively you can get an auxiliary battery system that charges from your engine but won't drain your starter battery if your engine is off. The latter is what I have done for the Pioneer PT mobile studio. This is a very good option.

I had originally seen a modified version of the performance trainer in the Keiser demo truck, that was shortened to fit in their demo van. Unfortunately the full height normal version is too tall to fit in the back of the vehicle, because the van slopes downward in the back. The normal height version is 87 inches. Due to the design and layout of my mobile studio I had to purchase a custom height functional trainer. This did come at a cost, but helps to legitimize the Pioneer PT operation. Currently there is one vehicle option available that should have sufficient height for a performance trainer without modification.

Mounting the performance trainer is next. The machine comes with mounting poles on the top and the bottom. To secure this, 100 pound beast, hardwood blocking was bolted inside the access holes above the door frame of the vehicle. This served as a secure place to attach the machine on the top, and then a stand was constructed up from the floor. This is where the machine was bolted into the floor on the bottom. This worked very well in securing the performance trainer into place and was a nice look at the back of the mobile studio, designating the "workout area." *** See picture above***

What about the air compressor? It could be installed inside, but would take up valuable space and cause increased noise, however, Sprinter vans have a lot of options for mounting things under the vehicle. Water tanks can be installed underneath, as well as the air compressor. Using stainless steel a custom mount was constructed to bolt the air compressor to the bottom of the vehicle. I recommend spray paint and stainless steel fasteners to help prevent rust.

Speaking of rust, the air compressor does have a drain on it, and it is recommended that you open the valve every so often to avoid moisture build up in the tank. This regular maintenance helps to prevent the tank from rusting out, and should be done more often in humid areas. Fortunately, it only takes about a minute to complete.

Then, once the air compressor is mounted, it becomes a little tricky. I had to run the air line from the compressor to the performance trainer inside the vehicle. The Sprinter is well thought out and does have access points under the van. I ran the air line along other wiring towards the back of the van, using zip ties to secure the line in place, and then removed an access portal near the wheel well, and fished the line up through the frame and into the back of the vehicle. This was pretty difficult, and requires some patience. Have help and a good flashlight so you can feed the line to another person. Listen to where it is going, because the air line can accidentally feed towards the wrong direction. The pressure gauge fits almost perfectly in the hole in the frame inside the vehicle and can be mounted adjacent to the performance trainer. Voila! You now have 80 pounds of resistance for training the entire body with different attachments. I utilize the handle, ankle strap, and chop bar most frequently.

To Do List:

- Decide machine or resistance bands
- Secure performance trainer, on board air compressor, and pressure switch.
- Secure materials to mount machine/ bands- stainless steel, bolts, bars, blocking
- Secure proper tools- screw gun, wrench

Step 13: Lettering

This again is optional. Your lawyer may tell you to keep your company name off the side of the truck so that if you ever get into an accident you would be less likely to be sued. Please do your homework and make the best decision for you and your business.

I chose to accept the risk and put my logo and company information on the sides and back of the vehicle for visual identification. It is known that a customer has to see something 8-10 x prior to making a purchase. I want to be everywhere! I want people to know who Pioneer PT is and what we can do for them. Due to the size of the vehicle, it is like a drivable billboard. People may begin to wonder who you are when they see you driving around town.

At the same time, don't drive like a jerk, because people will call your number to complain. I will tell you a quick story.

One day I was stuck trying to pull out of a parking lot, and no one would let me out. I was waiting forever to pull out, and then I saw my break. I thought I had plenty of space and went, but this guy deliberately accelerated to try to close down the gap, and not let me in. That is Baltimore drivers for you! It ended up being kind of close, but I didn't think anything of it. A minute later my phone began to ring, and I was excited because I thought it might be a new customer. I quickly realized it was the guy behind me, calling to complain about one of Pioneer PT's drivers. Haha!!! Come on dude! I listened, apologized, and said I would talk to the driver about it, even though I knew it was me. The guy continued to go on about it, so I finally said, "you know what, I have had problems with that guy in the past, I am going to fire him!" The guy on the phone, then began to backtrack telling me that it was not a problem and they guy did not deserve that. The moral of my story, is be patient when driving around, and give yourself extra time. You are representing your business with you name, logo, and number of the side of the vehicle, so be cool! There are a lot of jerks on the road that will speed up so that you cannot get in, cut in front of you, or attempt to speed around you. It will also take longer to get to your destination in a large mobile studio compared to a small car that you may be used to driving.

For this step, find a reputable business that specializes in lettering. Have them design a couple proofs, and choose the one you like best. Consider putting your logo, how you want to be contacted, and what you want to say on the vehicle. You may want to say who you help, as this grabs the attention of potential clients.

There are different types of lettering. You can have the vehicle wrapped, this can add color especially to a plain colored vehicle, and can even go over your windows providing increased privacy. Vinyl lettering is another option. I liked the color of my vehicle as it fit my logo and my business, so I picked a combination of both. However, if I had a white vehicle, I would have gone solely with a wrap.

<u>To Do List:</u>

- Find a local and reputable business that can help
- Decide what you want to put on the vehicle.
- Have them do a couple proofs on the computer
- Depending on personal comfort with risk and lawyers opinion- go for it!

Step 14: Congratulations:

Congratulations! You did it! You are now part of the tribe! #mobilestudiostrong

Now, it is real, and the journey is on! You have built a valuable piece of your business with hard-work, dedication, and imagination. Your mobile studio will serve as a tool that provides freedom to deliver convenient, preventive, and personalized care that will set you apart from everyone else in your space. You have no competition!

Next, if you have not already done so it is time to get out there to build relationships in your community, determine where your ideal client hangs out, give value, and help your client's where they need it most. Be patient, work hard, surround yourself with a supportive network, and don't forget to enjoy the ride!

Please share your journey with your community, and with the mobile studio tribe, so together we can help change our broken healthcare system. Change the status quo one client at a time by saying no to "sickcare" and hello to true preventive care. Prevent stories like what happened to Mr. Smith from happening again. Allow people to move well, and live well throughout their lives with personalized and convenient care when and where they need it!

About the author:

James Dulkerian, DPT is the owner of Pioneer PT, a concierge physical therapy and wellness practice in Baltimore, MD. James created the first mobile studio, a true clinic on wheels, to serve his clients when, and where they need it most. He is on a mission to share his dream, and help other health and wellness professionals around the world to take back control over their lifestyle, and find success treating their own rock star clients.